ROCKETBOARD

by Paul Collins

pencils by Matt Lin

inks by Natt Kattiyakulvanich

S   P   N

This 2010 edition published in the United Kingdom by
Scholastic Ltd
Book End
Range Road
Witney
Oxfordshire
OX29 0YD

First published in 2007 by
Macmillan Education Australia Pty Ltd.

Text by Paul Collins
Cover design by Allison Parry
Pencils by Matt Lin
Inks by Natt Kattiyakulvanich
Design by Matt Lin/Goblin Design

Out of this World: Rocketboard
ISBN 978-1407-11860-4

Printed by Ashford Colour Press Ltd

1 2 3 4 5 6 7 8 9   0 1 2 3 4 5 6 7 8 9

Contents

ROCKETBOARD

Characters

Spartans

Perry

Perry tries to be sensible – he really does.
But he can't say no to an adventure.

Fasool

Fasool is a hot-head. He often leads Perry into trouble –
if Perry doesn't lead him there first.

Sergeant Zach

Perry's uncle, he is one of the troopers who
patrol *Spartan*. He tries (but fails) to keep
the boys out of strife.

Mardi

Snookian

Mardi is an orphan from planet Snook. She's tough
as old boots – and the most loyal friend ever.

Other Folk

Sheaths and Daggers

The Darken twins, junior mobsters.

Cassandra Rake

The fastest torker on *Spartan*.
Until now.

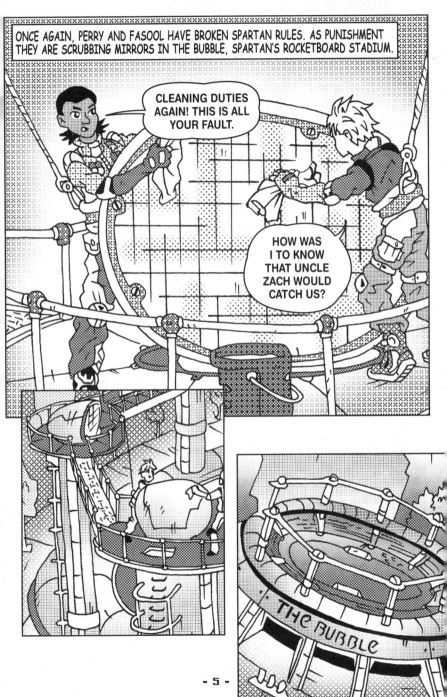

THE DOG STAR CARNIVAL IS COMING UP AND I'M HERE. HOW AM I SUPPOSED TO BACK THE WINNER?

WITH THE AMOUNT OF TIME YOU OWE THE TIMESTERS, I'M SURPRISED ANYONE WILL GIVE YOU CREDIT.

THAT'S JUST IT. IF I DON'T PLACE A BET I'M IN BIG TROUBLE.

I WARNED YOU AGAINST GAMBLING. YOU'LL NEVER COME OUT AHEAD.

I DON'T NEED A LECTURE. GRRR.

HOW MUCH TIME DO YOU OWE?

I OWE THE NEXT EIGHT YEARS OF MY LIFE TO THE DARKEN CLAN.

EIGHT YEARS? YOU CAN'T EVEN BUY YOURSELF OUT OF THAT MESS!

DAGGERS, CAN YOU SEE HIM?

THERE HERE IS, LET'S GO!

OUCH...

DO I FAINT NOW OR LATER?

OK, MAYBE LATER.

SLAP!

PERRY WATCHES THE TWINS RACING AFTER FASOOL.

TOWER 7

IF I WAS FASOOL, WHERE WOULD I BE... AH, OF COURSE!

SPARTAN IS HUGE. PERRY RUNS... AND RUNS...

ROCKETBOARD STORAGE ▶

SOME PEOPLE JUST NEVER LEARN.

STOP TELLING ME WHAT TO DO! CASSANDRA RAKE CAN'T LOSE. I'VE BET THE REST OF MY LIFE ON HER – I HAD TO, SHE'S ODDS-ON FAVOURITE TO WIN.

IT'LL CLEAR MY DEBTS. THEN IT'S NO MORE GAMBLING FOR ME.

ER, IN CASE YOU DIDN'T NOTICE, MARDI'S ENTERED THE CONTEST. WITH HER ROCK-HOPPING EXPERIENCE, SHE'S A SURE-FIRE WINNER.

THERE'S NO WAY I'M RISKING MY TIME ON AN UNTRIED FIRST-TIMER.

YOU SHOW IT FOR BOTH OF US. ME? I'M BANKING ON CASSANDRA.

WE'VE GOT TO SHOW MARDI SOME SUPPORT.

WHEN I SAY 'SUPPORT' I MEAN FRIENDSHIP, NOT GAMBLING.

IF YOU TWO 'BOYS' HAVE FINISHED CHATTING, I BELIEVE WE HAVE SOME UNFINISHED BUSINESS...

IT'S MY LIFE, PERRY. AFTER TODAY, I'LL BE A FREE MAN.

TO CASSANDRA RAKE – THE FASTEST TORKER ON SPARTAN!

I HOPE YOU'RE RIGHT, FASOOL. I REALLY DO.

SUDDENLY, PERRY SEES...

ER, UNLESS YOU CAN RUN AS FAST AS YOU LOSE AT GAMBLING, YOU'LL NEVER GET TO COLLECT YOUR WINNINGS. HERE COME THE DARKEN TWINS.

YIPES!

THE TWINS ARRIVE – A FEW SECONDS TOO LATE.

- 12 -

FASOOL AND PERRY GET SAFELY BACK TO THE BUBBLE.

HUFF, HUFF, COME ON, PERRY!

COMING THROUGH.

WATCH IT, KID!

SORRY!

EXCUSE ME.

MY TOES!

PARDON.

HALF AN HOUR LATER, AND WITH ONLY MOMENTS TO SPARE BEFORE THE FIRST RACE, OUR HEROES FALL INTO THEIR SEATS.

DO YOU THINK WE LOST THEM?

PUT IT THIS WAY, IF SOMEONE JUST TOUCHES ME ON THE SHOULDER I THINK I'M GOING TO DIE.

GREAT. JUST GREAT. THIS IS ANOTHER FINE MESS YOU'VE GOT US INTO.

CALM DOWN, PERRY. AFTER CASSANDRA WINS THE RACE, I'LL BE A FREE MAN.

CASSANDRA RAKE IS QUICKSILVER!

CASSANDRA... SHE'S THE BEST...

YOU STILL DON'T GET IT, DO YOU? YOUR FUTURE IS FORFEIT. WHOEVER COLLECTS ON YOU WILL PROBABLY HAVE YOU SCRUBBING OUT THE SANITARY PUMPS.

YE OF LITTLE FAITH, PERRY...

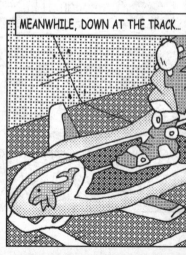

MEANWHILE, DOWN AT THE TRACK...

THE FIRST EVENT IS ABOUT TO START. IT'S A TEAM MATCH. EACH ROCKETBOARD HAS TO CIRCLE THE TRACK ONCE, CHANGE DRIVER, THEN DO ANOTHER LAP.

PERRY AND FASOOL'S HOME TEAM, THE HUMPBACKS, HAVE ENTERED.

VERRRRRRRRRRRRRRRRRRRRRRRRRRRRR

GO, HUMPBACKS!

KEEP YOUR VOICE DOWN, PERRY.

OK, MR GAMBLER, WHO WOUL[D] YOU CHEE[R] FOR IN TH[E] RACE?

NOT THE HUMPBACKS. THAT'S YOUR PROBLEM, PERRY. YOU LET LOYALTY AND EMOTION GET IN THE WAY.

ANSWER MY QUESTION. YOU'RE BACKING...?

THE SNORKS. THEY'RE THE BEST SHORT-DISTANCE SPRINTERS IN THE LEAGUE.

GONG!

SHERWARGH!

THERE GOES ANY CHANCE OF THE SNORKS WINNING THE FIRST HEAT...

LOOK ON THE BRIGHT SIDE. YOU COULD HAVE BET YOUR FUTURE ON THIS RACE.

SHUT UP, PERRY. IT WAS JUST BAD LUCK.

GAMBLING'S FULL OF 'IF' STORIES, FASOOL. SORRY TO SAY IT, BUT GAMBLING'S A SUCKER'S GAME.

MUMBLE, GRUMBLE...

HOLLY

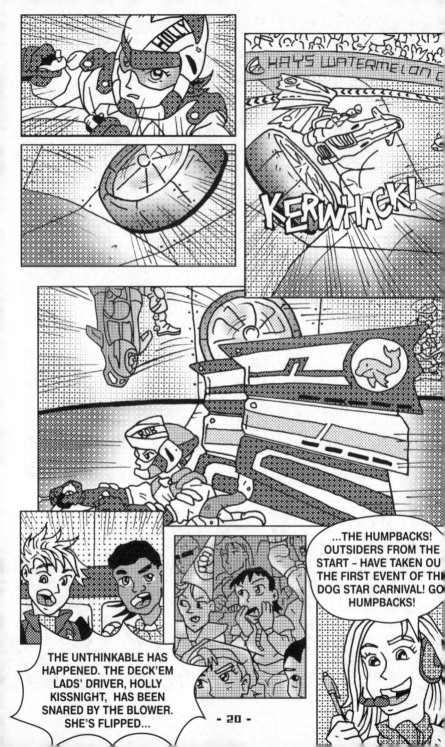

- 20 -

WHOOSH!

DON'T SAY A WORD, PERRY. NOT A WORD.

IT'S TIME FOR THE SOLO EVENT. MARDI IS ONE OF SIX CONTESTANTS.

RELAX, THERE'S NO WAY SHEATHS AND DAGGERS CAN SEE US IN THIS CROWD. BESIDES, THEY WOULDN'T THINK WE'RE STUPID ENOUGH TO BE HERE.

ER, JUST TO ROCK YOUR WORLD A LITTLE...

GREAT VIEW, FASOOL. THANKS A LOT.

IT'S NOT YOU THEY'RE AFTER!

FASOOL POINTS INTO THE CROWD...

...BACK TO WHERE THEY JUST CAME FROM, WHERE THE TWINS ARE NOW ASKING FOR THEM!

WELL, IF THE TWINS CAN FOLLOW THOSE DIRECTIONS WE DESERVE TO BE CAUGHT.

SPEAK FOR YOURSELF, PERRY.

FOLKS, THE MAIN EVENT IS ABOUT TO BEGIN. SIX CONTESTANTS, 21 TIGHTLY CONTESTED EVENTS OVER THE NEXT THREE DAYS!

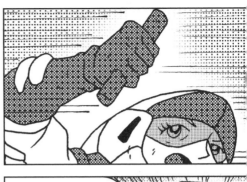

WHAT'S HAPPENING? HOLLY ALREADY HAS A PEG AND CASSANDRA HASN'T EVEN TAKEN OFF!

MAYBE HOLLY JUST GOT A LUCKY BREAK. SHAME THOUGH THAT CASSANDRA CAME UP AGAINST HER IN THE FIRST RACE. LOOK! CASSANDRA HAS STARTED.

YIKES. HOLLY JUST DUMPED TWO PEGS IN A ROW TO CASSANDRA'S ZERO!

HOLLY 2
CASS 0

SHERWOOSH

45 SECONDS GONE - HOLLY 5 PEGS, CASSANDRA 2 PEGS.

I HATE TO SAY THIS, BUT KISSNIGHT WAS INJURED IN THE LAST EVENT. IMAGINE WHAT SHE'D BE DOING IF SHE HADN'T BEEN.

CASS IS PLAYING WITH HER. YOU WAIT AND SEE.

1 MINUTE, 15 SECONDS GONE - HOLLY 10 PEGS, CASSANDRA 7 PEGS.

2 MINUTES, 52 SECONDS GONE - HOLLY 20 PEGS, CASSANDRA 19 PEGS.

3 MINUTES GONE - FINAL SCORE HOLLY 20 PEGS, CASSANDRA 21 PEG

I THINK I'M GOING TO FAINT.

AND THIS IS ONLY THE FIRST HEAT...

LADIES AND GENTLEMEN - IT DOESN'T GET MOR EXCITING THAN TH THE ROUND GOES CASSANDRA RAKE A LENGTH! NOW FO A SHORT BREAK.

HALF AN HOUR LATER.

RELAX FASOOL. THERE'S NO WAY ANYONE'S GOING TO SPOT US HERE.

THAT'S EASY FOR YOU TO SAY.

I'M THE ONE WHO'S GOING TO SPEND THE BEST YEARS OF MY LIFE IN THE SUMP STATION IF I'M CAUGHT.

THE SECOND SOLO EVENT IS A STRAIGHT RACE. SPRINTING ON THE OUTSIDE IS SLOWER THAN THE INSIDE, BUT THE INSIDE RAILS ARE PRONE TO SUDDEN GUSTS OF WIND.

FOR YOUR ENTERTAINMENT WE HAVE MARDI TANTHORPE, OUR ONLY FIRST-TIME CONTESTANT, UP AGAINST VETERAN ROCKETBOARDER, MINI B'NASH.

SO YOU'RE REALLY HOPING MARDI LOSES THIS EVENT.

IT'S NOT AS SIMPLE AS THAT.

- 30 -

THEY'VE REACHED THE HALFWAY MARK! LOOKS LIKE MINI HAS IT IN THE BAG!

SUDDENLY...

HUH?

MARDI DOESN'T HAVE A -

LOOK! MINI'S FORGOTTEN ALL ABOUT THE TURBINE. SHE'S TOO BUSY LOOKING BACK AT MARDI.

SHERWISH!

- 33 -

FIFTEEN SCARY MINUTES LATER.

THEY'VE GONE. PHEW.

DON'T PHEW TOO SOON. THERE ARE STILL TWO DAYS LEFT TO GO.

I'VE GOT AN IDEA. LET'S GO SEE MARDI.

ARE YOU CRAZY?

IT'S THE LAST THING THEY'LL EXPECT.

THE BOYS FIND MARDI SIGNING AUTOGRAPHS.

HEY GUYS. TORKING IS JUST SO MUCH FUN. IT'S EASY-PEASY.

THAT'S GREAT. ISN'T IT FASOOL?

MUMBLE, GRUMBLE.

WHY DO I GET THE FEELING YOU'RE NOT HAPPY FOR ME?

FASOOL HAS A CONFESSION TO MAKE, HAVEN'T YOU, MR 'HOT TIP'?

OK, OK. SO I GAMBLED MY LIFE ON CASSANDRA.

I OWED EIGHT YEARS ANYWAY! IF I'D QUIT I'D HAVE STILL BEEN IN TROUBLE!

AND IF YOU HADN'T GAMBLED IN THE FIRST PLACE YOU'D BE LAUGHING RIGHT NOW. GRRRR.

WELL, CASSANDRA HAS TWO DAYS LEFT TO IMPROVE HERSELF. BUT WHAT WILL YOU DO IF SHE DOESN'T WIN?

RESIGN MYSELF TO SMELLING LIKE A SKUNK RAT FOR THE REST OF MY LIFE, I GUESS.

BETWEEN US WE'LL THINK OF SOMETHING, FASOOL. THOSE TIMESTERS HAVEN'T GOT HOLD OF YOU YET!

OK...

WE'D BETTER GET BACK TO THE HUMP. AT LEAST WE'LL BE SAFE UNTIL TOMORROW.

DON'T YOU BOYS GO AND DO ANYTHING SILLY.

AS IF YOU REALLY CARE, MUMBLE, GRUMBLE...

DAY TWO OF THE SOLO. IT'S PROVING TO BE A DISASTER. AT THIS POINT, THERE IS ONLY ONE RACE LEFT.

THERE GOES BRASSNECK DAWKINS! HOW MANY ACCIDENTS IS THAT IN A DAY'S ROCKETBOARDING?

- 37 -

SETTLE DOWN, FASOOL.

LEAVE ME ALONE. I CAN SEE STARS. IT'S PROBABLY THE LAST TIME I'LL EVER SEE THEM.

GURGLE, SPLUTTER. IT'S OVER.

COME ON, FASOOL...

SNAP OUT...

OF IT!

LISTEN! SO MARDI IS LEADING BY A FEW POINTS. SO MOST OF THE COMPETITION HAS BEEN INJURED. SO THERE'S ONLY A FEW EVENTS LEFT TODAY FOR CASSANDRA TO CATCH UP.

AND WHAT IF THE TWINS ARE SCOURING THE BUBBLE LOOKING FOR US? IT COULD GET WORSE -

OH, YES? HOW CAN IT GET WORSE?

ER... MAYBE THE TWINS COULD FIND US. OR...

DON'T EVEN JOKE ABOUT THAT!

WELL, MARDI DIDN'T WIN. THAT MEANS: A) SHE'S NOT ANOTHER POINT AHEAD OF CASSANDRA, AND B) MAYBE SHE'S FLAGGING.

SUDDENLY...

FASOOL!

UH-OH. HERE WE GO AGAIN.

DO YOU EVER FEEL LIKE YOU'RE LIVING THE SAME DAY OVER AGAIN?

LET'S GET OUT OF HERE!

AFTER A NIGHT SPENT HIDING FROM THE DARKEN TWINS, FASOOL AND PERRY FINALLY ARRIVE AT THE ROCKETBOARDERS' PAVILION.

WE DIDN'T SEE THE LAST RACE. WHAT HAPPENED?

I GUESS MINI WAS BETTER ON THE DAY.

SHE SEEMED AMAZED THAT SHE'D WON.

WELL, I HOPE EVERYONE'S RECOVERED FROM THEIR INJURIES. I'D HATE TO WIN THE SOLO BY DEFAULT.

YEAH, THAT WOULD BE A DISASTER.

FASOOL PEERS THROUGH THE CURTAIN...

ARGH!

BLAH BLAH BLAH BLAH BLAH.

ARGH!

BLAH BLAH BLAH BLAH BLAH BLAH... BLAH.

OUTSIDE.

OH NO...

WELL, IF IT ISN'T YOUNG FASOOL. THE ONE THAT OWES US EIGHT YEARS OF HIS LIFE.

YOU'RE COMING WITH US, LOSER. HEHEHE!

GULP. HEY GUYS, I CAN EXPLAIN!

WHADDYA SAY, DAGGERS?

I HATE TO SEE A KID GET WRONG-SIDED BY GAMBLING.

I SAY WE GIVE HIM A CHANCE TO WIPE THE SLATE CLEAN.

OK KID. YOU'VE GOT A MINUTE TO SING LIKE A CANARY.

I'LL REMIND YOU IT AIN'T HEALTHY BREATHIN' SEWAGE SMELLS FOR EIGHT YEARS STRAIGHT -

ER, WHEN DOES MY MINUTE START? YOU'VE JUST TAKEN UP 20 SECONDS OF IT.

OUCH!

THEN YOU'D BETTER MAKE SURE SHE LOSES, KID. BECAUSE YOUR CASSANDRA HAD BETTER WIN. COMPRENDE?

OR IT'S CURTAINS FOR YOU, LOSER.

GULP!

WHAT'S GOING ON HERE?

WE'VE LEFT ALREADY.

WE WERE JUST LEAVING.

REMEMBER KID. THE ROCK-HOPPER MARDI STANTHORPE LOSES, OR YOU LOSE –

BIG TIME.

FIVE MINUTES LATER, FASOOL PLEADING WITH MARDI TO ROW IN THE SOLO RACE.

ARE YOU FINISHED PLEADING YET?

ALMOST, GULP. IT'S NOT SUCH A BIG THING TO ASK. NO ONE EXPECTS YOU TO WIN ANYWAY!

GRRRR. IT WOULD SERVE YOU RIGHT IF YOU LOSE EIGHT YEARS OF YOUR LIFE IN THE SEWAGE LINE, FASOOL.

YOU SHOULD NEVER GAMBLE - MUCH LESS GAMBLE WHAT YOU CAN'T AFFORD TO LOSE. FOR THE RECORD, CHEATS ARE LOSERS AS WELL.

WHAT ARE YOU GOING TO DO?

I'M GOING TO RACE LIKE NEVER BEFORE.

ARGH! STARS... I SEE STARS AGAIN!

- 47 -